THE KING'S
COMPUTER

by Larry Podlezak
illustrated by Christiane Beauregard

SCHOOL PUBLISHERS

Printed in China

ISBN 10: 0-15-350515-X
ISBN 13: 978-0-15-350515-7

Ordering Options
ISBN 10: 0-15-350334-3 (Grade 4 Below-Level Collection)
ISBN 13: 978-0-15-350334-4 (Grade 4 Below-Level Collection)
ISBN 10: 0-15-357505-0 (package of 5)
ISBN 13: 978-0-15-357505-1 (package of 5)

4 5 6 7 8 9 10   0940   12 11 10 09

Characters

KING MARTIN	**BILL BARCLAY**
QUEEN WANDA	**JACK JONES**
GIANT	**SALLY**
PRINCE ALFRED	**THE MAIL CARRIER**
ANNIE THOMAS	**MAN**

Setting: KING MARTIN'S *office*

KING MARTIN *(at his computer)***:**
Another victory for the king!
I'm so happy I could sing!

QUEEN WANDA:
Having more computer fun,
Even though your work's not done?

KING MARTIN:
Oh, my queen, I have to play!
I can't sit on my throne all day.

QUEEN WANDA:
As you wish, this is our house.
Feel free to click that silly mouse.
(QUEEN WANDA *exits angrily.*)

KING MARTIN:

I don't see why the queen should care
if I enjoy some good software.
We both take care of our kingdom,
So why can't I stop and have some fun?

GIANT (*Offstage*)**:**

I want to use that computer, too.
I know what CD-ROMs can do.

KING MARTIN:

Oh, my, I think I'm hearing things.
(GIANT's *large hand reaches through the window.*)
I see huge fingers and some rings!

GIANT:

Hello, your Highness, it is I,
a giant taller than the sky.

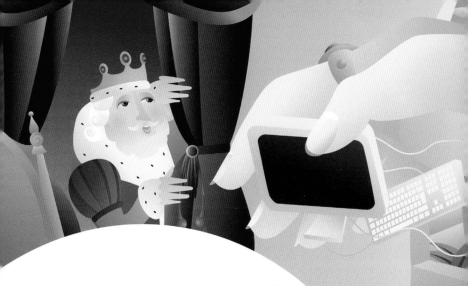

(GIANT's *hand picks up* computer.)

KING MARTIN (*Frightened*):

Giant, sir, please let me be!

Whatever could you want from me?

GIANT:

Your laptop, your scanner,

your printer and cable.

Your disk drive, your mouse pad,

your computer table.

(GIANT *takes computer equipment out through the window.*)

KING MARTIN (*Upset*):

What a bad experience!

I'll never be the same!

Now I won't get my highest score,

and this giant is to blame!

(PRINCE ALFRED *rushes into the room.*)

PRINCE ALFRED:
Father, are you all right?
I heard a large intruder!

KING MARTIN:
Yes, but that big beast went
and stole my new computer.

QUEEN WANDA (*Happily*):
Your computer ceases to exist?
My heart is filled with glee!
Now perhaps you'll have more time
to help me run our property!

KING MARTIN (*to* PRINCE ALFRED):
Go make a big announcement.
Tell all of the kingdom this:
Whoever brings my computer back
I will make very rich!

6

SETTING:

*The foothills
of a large mountain
(ANNIE THOMAS
and MAN are looking
up at the mountain.)*

ANNIE THOMAS:

Now listen, my friend,
and I'll tell you the plan.
We climb up there nimbly,
as quick as we can.

MAN: And then?

ANNIE THOMAS:

We take the computer.
We go see the king,
and, before you know it,
we own everything!

(THE MAIL CARRIER *enters.*)

THE MAIL CARRIER:

Sorry, pals, I overheard your plan.
The giant no longer lives on this land.

SETTING: *Inside a cave*

(BILL BARCLAY *is shining his flashlight in the cave as he walks.*)

BILL BARCLAY:

I'll find that giant deep in this cave.

Bill Barclay knows how giants behave!

Then when I take his computer away,

he'll probably cry for a couple of days.

Bill Barclay, though, will start to sing,

since he'll get a fortune from the king.

Come on out, giant, show your face!

(THE MAIL CARRIER *enters.*)

THE MAIL CARRIER:

Excuse me. The giant doesn't live in this place.

(BILL BARCLAY *looks at him, disappointed.*)

(JACK JONES *and a small group are walking with ropes in their hands.*)

JACK JONES:

That giant is fierce—he must live out here,
along with the snakes and the bobcats and deer.

(THE MAIL CARRIER *enters.*)

THE MAIL CARRIER:

Well, finally, someone who reads the address!
You're on the right track, I have to confess.

(*Loud footsteps are heard offstage.*)

JACK JONES:

That's him—he's returning! He's on his way back!
Get all the ropes ready! Prepare to attack!

GIANT (*Offstage*)**:**

Move!

(JACK JONES *and* MEN
scream and run away.)

SETTING SALLY's *bedroom*:

SALLY (*Sitting at her computer*):
I think I know how to solve this case.
I'll look for the giant in cyberspace.
I'll write him an e-mail at giant.rom.
Perhaps he's got his computer on.

(*Typing on the computer while speaking*)
Dear Giant, How are you? How have you been?
Are you enjoying your new machine?
Giant, please answer. You need not be shy.
I really would like to receive your reply.

(*She clicks her mouse and instantly hears a beep.*)

COMPUTER VOICE:
You have mail!

SALLY (*Excited*):
The giant responded! He writes pretty fast!
I know his location. I've found him at last!

SETTING: *The next morning at the king's castle*
(SALLY *is standing before* KING MARTIN.)

SALLY:

I know where the giant is hiding, your Highness.
I'll tell you as long as you keep your promise.

KING MARTIN:

The best people couldn't find him?
Not Bill, Jack, or Annie?
Your detective skills are slick and uncanny.

SALLY:

It's a trait, I believe, I get from my mom.
The others did not search at giant.rom.

KING MARTIN (*Happy*):

Young girl, you're amazing!
I'm very impressed.
You'll get your fortune!
You'll have only the best!

11

SETTING: *Outside the offices of giant.rom*
(ANNIE THOMAS, BILL BARCLAY, *and* JACK JONES *are standing outside the building.*)

ANNIE THOMAS:
What's taking Sally so long?
Maybe something has gone wrong!

BILL BARCLAY:
He might think she's a stranger.
Then she'd really be in danger!

(Loud footsteps are heard offstage. They stop, and then Sally appears carrying a computer.)

JACK JONES (*Relieved*)**:**
There she is! She did it!
The computer's in her hands.
The king will be so happy.
He'll be her biggest fan!

(SALLY *hands over the computer.*)

SALLY:

The giant isn't terrible.

He really isn't mean.

He took the king's computer

because his own was being cleaned.

BILL BARCLAY:

You mean he's just impatient?

He doesn't like to wait?

SALLY:

He didn't want his friends to think

he sent out e-mails late.

SETTING: *The king's castle later that day*
(KING MARTIN *is sitting in his office, happily playing on his computer.*)

QUEEN WANDA (*Angry*):
Now that you have your toy back,
I know where you will be:
typing at your keyboard
and ignoring your duties.

KING MARTIN:
My dear, you are mistaken!
Please do not distress!
I've just set up for each of us
a new e-mail address!
E-mail will help us now
to get all of our work done,
and then we can both go out
and have a little fun!

Think Critically

1. Do you think the author of this play likes computers? Explain your answer.

2. What did King Martin do to get his computer back?

3. What is the setting at the beginning of the play? How does it change throughout the play?

4. How would you describe Sally?

5. What part of the play did you think was the funniest?

 Language Arts

Write a Summary Write a paragraph that tells what happened in this play. Be sure to include the key events that took place.

School-Home Connection Tell a family member about this play. Then have a discussion about how to be a good problem solver.

Word Count: 1,011